H

Heavy Weather

Martyn Turner

Gill and Macmillan

Published in Ireland by
Gill and Macmillan Ltd
Goldenbridge
Dublin 8
with associated companies in
Auckland, Delhi, Gaborone, Hamburg, Harare,
Hong Kong, Johannesburg, Kuala Lumpur, Lagos, London,
Manzini, Melbourne, Mexico City, Nairobi,
New York, Singapore, Tokyo

© Martyn Turner 1989
0 7171 1699 9
Print origination by Typeworkshop, Dublin
Printed in Hong Kong

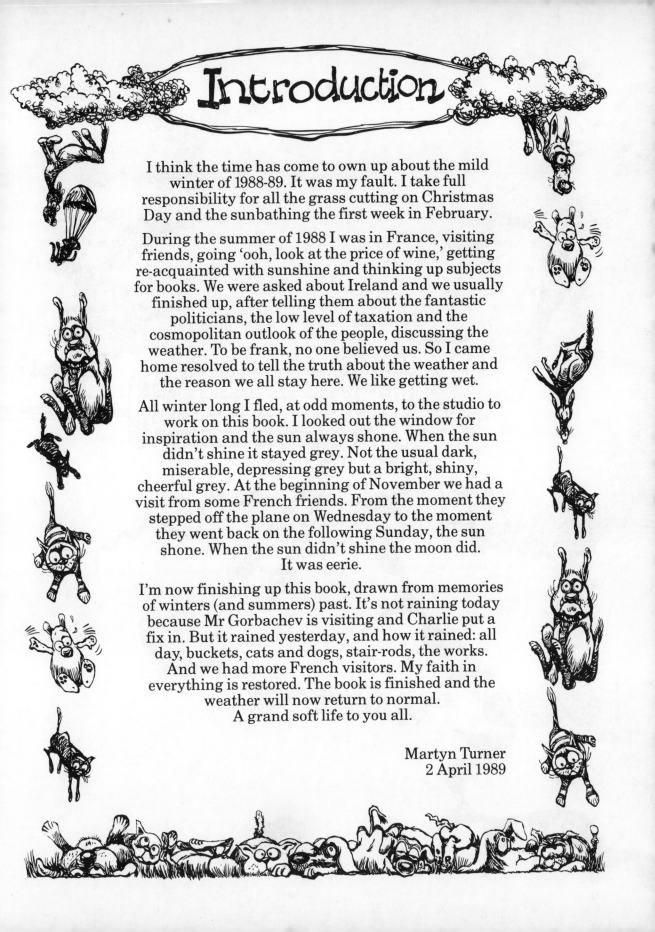

Introduction

I think the time has come to own up about the mild winter of 1988-89. It was my fault. I take full responsibility for all the grass cutting on Christmas Day and the sunbathing the first week in February.

During the summer of 1988 I was in France, visiting friends, going 'ooh, look at the price of wine,' getting re-acquainted with sunshine and thinking up subjects for books. We were asked about Ireland and we usually finished up, after telling them about the fantastic politicians, the low level of taxation and the cosmopolitan outlook of the people, discussing the weather. To be frank, no one believed us. So I came home resolved to tell the truth about the weather and the reason we all stay here. We like getting wet.

All winter long I fled, at odd moments, to the studio to work on this book. I looked out the window for inspiration and the sun always shone. When the sun didn't shine it stayed grey. Not the usual dark, miserable, depressing grey but a bright, shiny, cheerful grey. At the beginning of November we had a visit from some French friends. From the moment they stepped off the plane on Wednesday to the moment they went back on the following Sunday, the sun shone. When the sun didn't shine the moon did. It was eerie.

I'm now finishing up this book, drawn from memories of winters (and summers) past. It's not raining today because Mr Gorbachev is visiting and Charlie put a fix in. But it rained yesterday, and how it rained: all day, buckets, cats and dogs, stair-rods, the works. And we had more French visitors. My faith in everything is restored. The book is finished and the weather will now return to normal. A grand soft life to you all.

Martyn Turner
2 April 1989

An explanatory guide to Ireland....

....and its weather

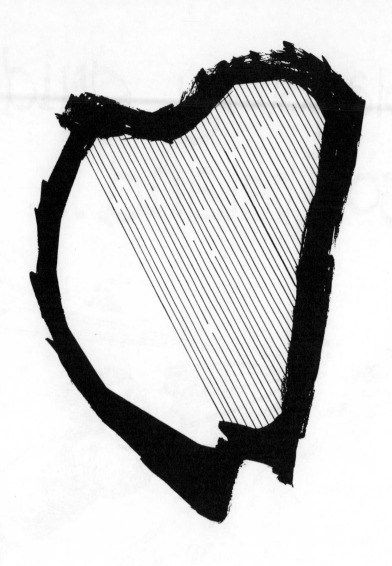

This is the symbol of Ireland...

...this is the reason.

Most of the weather in Ireland...

...comes from the west.

NOTES FOR VISITORS, TOURISTS, ALIENS ETC.

You have probably heard in your geography lessons at school that Ireland has a sun problem. This is the problem that is the main subject of this small book. The following few brief words have two intentions. Firstly, they will explain to you some of the items of clothing and suchlike that may be strange to you but will crop up throughout the book. Secondly, if you are reading this outside Ireland you may use this brief explanation as a hands-on/up-to-the-minute/cordon bleu guide to the sort of tropical kit that every visitor to Ireland should include in his/her baggage.

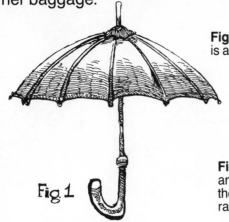

Fig. 1 SUNSHADE. This is this-here-yoke and is an essential item to be carried at all times.

Fig. 2 SUN-HAT. Again an essential item to keep those ultraviolet killer rays off the pate.

Fig. 3 GOGGLES. It may seem more normal for sun-glasses to be worn. However in Ireland dark glasses have political connotations which can cause the unwary visitor to come into contact with such exotic and basically unattractive institutions as the Special Criminal Court, the Offences Against the State Act and their counterparts in the northern part of our country. Thus we recommend dark goggles as a suitable substitute.

Fig. 4 SCARF. Ronald Reagan visited Ireland in 1982 and did nothing to protect his nose from our climate. In 1987 he underwent surgery for nasal skin cancer. To avoid similar tragedies, keep your face covered at all times by a nice warm Donegal wool scarf.

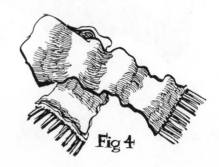

Fig. 5 BODY COVER. Such all-over garments are available throughout Ireland in rubberised or plasticised yellow polyputhekettlon.

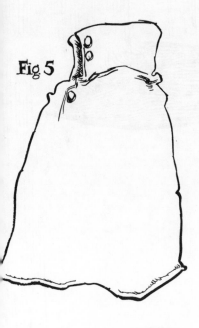

Fig 5

Fig. 6

Fig. 6 BOOTS. A good pair of knee-high rubber boots is essential for the visitor to avoid any risk from snake bite. So effective are these boots, worn at all times by everyone in Ireland, that no one in Ireland has ever suffered a snake bite.

Foreign visitors should take appropriate measures in the event of rain.

Mexicans should not siesta outdoors.

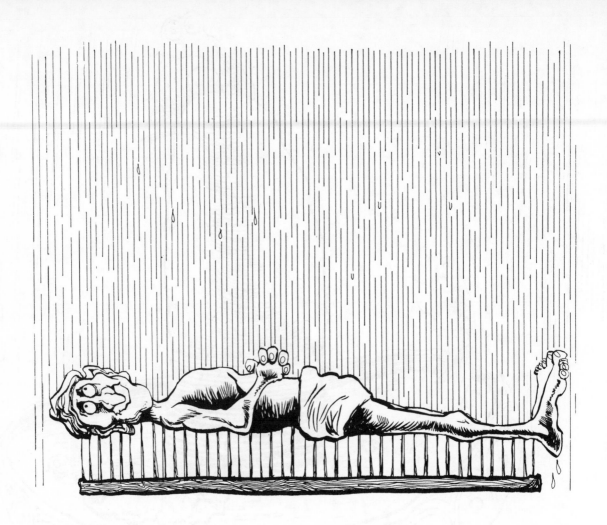

Some may enjoy outdoor living...

...and others may think a little rain is worth diamonds.

Visitors would do well...

...to learn our road signs,

(although they are not always reliable).

But you <u>can</u> always rely on our professional weather forecasters.

1. Warm Front

2. Cold Front

3. Three cold fronts and 6 warm fronts together

They use the standard weather symbols...

...and keep you informed of the passing seasons.

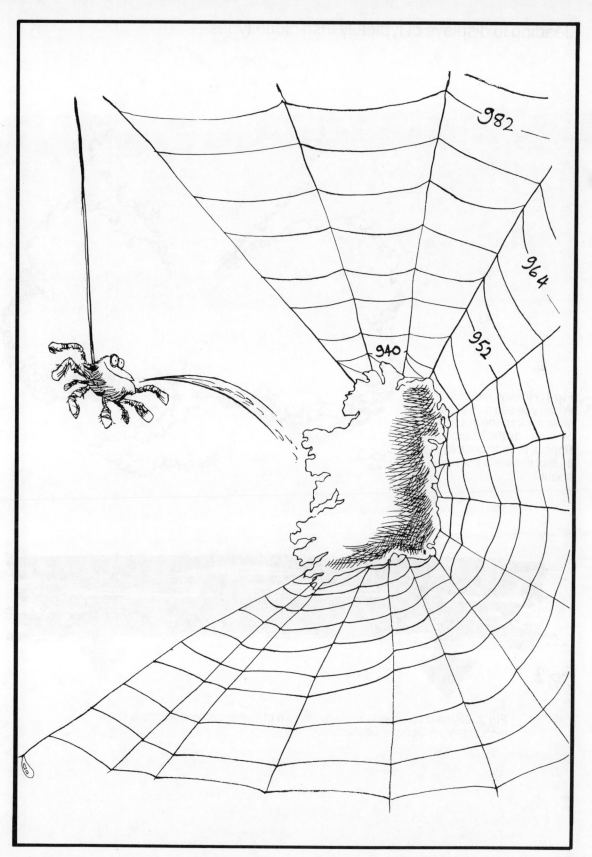

...leading to displays of typically Irish cloud types.

Fig 1. Hiberno nimbus. When you see its typical shamrock shape you can be sure - as the Liverpool Special Branch quaintly put it - that there is a shower about.

Fig 1.

Fig. 2.

Fig 2. Layered cloud which produces rain of immense proportions is known, technically, as Serious Stratus.

Fig 3. An almost-unique-to-Ireland cloud type (as the grammatical would say) last seen at Ballinspittle, County Cork; this is a common sky after a heavy session in the church or in the pub, or both. A moving experience.

Dublin in winter doesn't always get rain.

Sometimes they have smog.

The weather can be blamed for the economic plight of the country...

If a cow is lying down it's about to rain...

If it's standing up it's lying.

...and other things, the subject of almost traditional sayings...

"When the T.D.s fly away for the summer, can the autumn session be hardly more than 4 months behind..."

...about politics,

Autumn leaves – T.D. arrives....

Red sky at night,
Too much delight.

social life,

The rain on the Irish plain,
Falls mainly on
Bungalows of Spain

and architecture.

The weather influences wild life...

...and domesticated life, too.

Irish Holidaymaker

And, while it leads to a certain similarity in appearance...

Irish Nudist

...among the natives...

...it in no way affects our generosity of spirit.

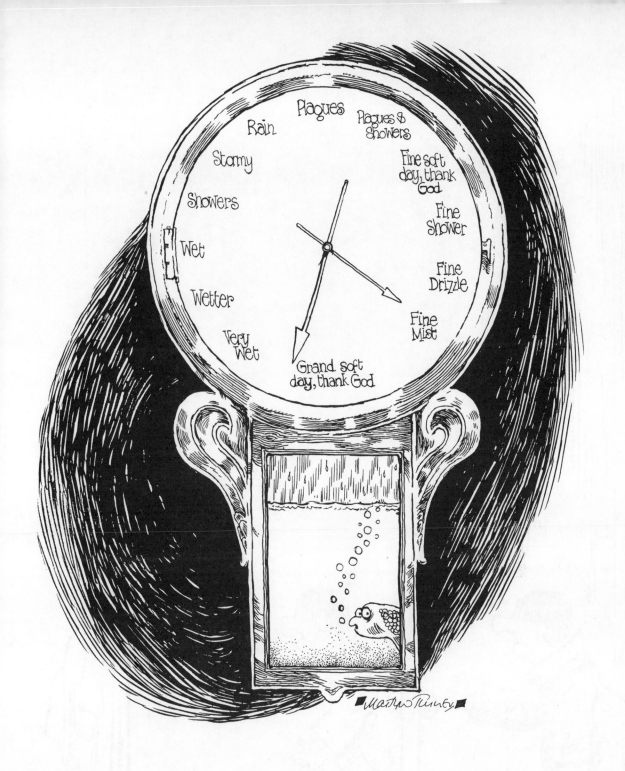

Some really Wet strip cartoons

46

...WHO THOUGHT THEY KNEW. THEY WEREN'T FROM THE VILLAGE.

THREE NINE ELEVEN TWO HALF

THEY WERE FROM THE MOUNTAIN OF PERPETUAL FOG AND CLOUD.

ONCE OR TWICE A YEAR THEY WOULD DESCEND THROUGH THE FOG.....

... AND POKE AROUND THE VILLAGE EXAMINING, COUNTING AND LOOKING.

48

THE FOLLOWING MORNING THEY WOULD TELL THE VILLAGE WHAT WOULD HAPPEN IN THE NEXT YEAR (AND EXPLAIN WHY WHAT THEY SAID WOULD HAPPEN THIS YEAR DIDN'T HAPPEN, EVEN THOUGH THEY SAID IT WOULD).

FOR THIS SERVICE THE VILLAGE WOULD SHELL OUT MIGHTY FEES.

THEY WOULD THEN GO BACK TO WHERE THEY LIVED IN THE CLOUDS, UNTIL THE FOLLOWING YEAR.

SOME PEOPLE THOUGHT THAT THESE MEN WERE ONTO A BIT OF A SCAM. SO THEY CALLED THEM **THE 'CON 'O' MISTS**

1.

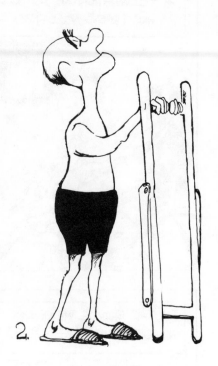

2.

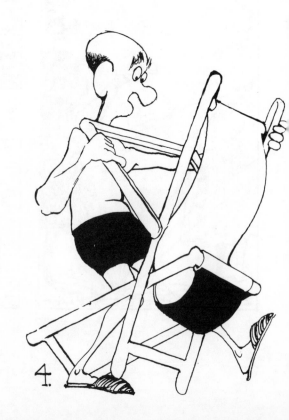

4.

3.

5.

6.

7.

8.

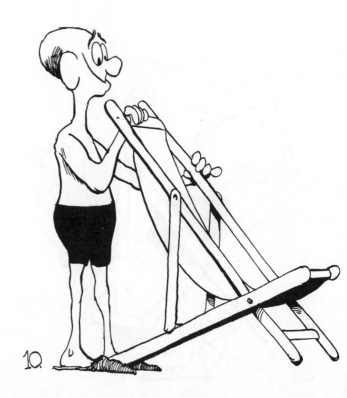

10.

9.

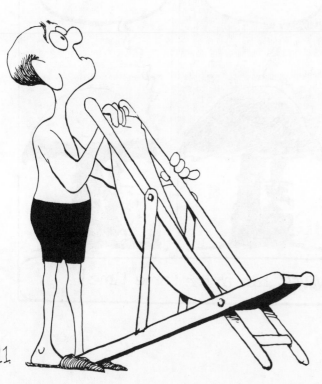

11.

12.

53

THINGS WEREN'T QUITE RIGHT IN THE MYSTICAL MAGIC LAND OF THE LEPRECHAUNS.

Things aren't quite right in our magical land of the leprechauns....

It's either raining..

Or it's sunny...

NEVER both at the same time!

NO IDEAS. NOT A ONE. ZILCH. THEN, SUDDENLY, THREE DAYS LATER A QUEER CLASS OF A CLOUD CAME UPON THEM.

THE CLOUD CLEARED...

REVEALING...

..AND GREETING

A VERY STRANGE MAN: COMPLETELY LACKING IN A SILLY HAT OF ANY KIND.

Yo!

I've heard of your light problem! It's heavy! I've got your solution! I've got your man!

Strength, bravery, brains... well, two out of three ain't bad. He has sweat, he has muscle, he has blood, he has the power (for you) to unite the sun and the rain!

He is....

A few weathery bits of Irish history

How the island of Ireland...

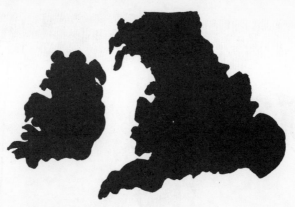

5,900 b.c.

...was formed.

The early Irish worshipped the sun.....

...but after a couple of centuries there was no evidence it existed....

...so they moved on to worship something more tangible.

Early design work on...

...the Book of Kells.

The Vikings were successful...

...thanks to better technology.

The Flight of the Earls...

...and the weather that kept them away.

King Billy at the Boyne.

Sir Walter Raleigh. A rare example of an Englishman trying to help Ireland.

The babyhood of the Duke of Wellington.

Easter, 1916.

De Valera at a rally.

Ulster Says Noah.

Scenes from weather future

HOW TO COMBAT THE GREENHOUSE EFFECT

1.
Take all recent articles, pamphlets, books etc. on the Greenhouse Effect and put them in your roof space. This is the most effective use of many of these pieces as, used in this way, they will cut down your fuel use by making your house warmer. This will reduce the CO_2 emissions from your house, the main cause of the Greenhouse Effect.

2.
Encourage more nuclear power. As well as decreasing CO_2 emissions into the atmosphere from traditional power stations, the inevitable nuclear accidents will lead to vast losses of life which will, consequently, lead to further decreases in houses and thus less fuel and thus less CO_2.

3.
A two in one offer. Have nothing to do with people who use ozone unfriendly products (see a few pages ahead). As well as being environmentally sound a decrease in social intercourse will, eventually, lead to a decrease in the population, and thus a decrease in homes and thus a decrease in CO_2 emissions. Simple, eh?

The Greenhouse Effect will cause a dramatic rise in sea level.
In Northern Ireland there may be a shift in economic power when
the lowlands of the plantation are flooded...

2.

3

but, there may not.

Curiously, predictions suggest that the Greenhouse Effect will, unlike elsewhere, make Ireland colder and wetter. Bord Fáilte will at long last be able to be unbelievably honest in its advertising.

Ireland

Magic, Mud and Monsoons

After 1992, BAR'O'METRIC PRESSURE will be on the rise,

and the new world of technology will rain down on us all.

We will worry some more about the OZONE LAYER...

...and lots more about airborne and sea-borne pollution from Sellafield.

In politics, the forecasts will stay miserable (except for the forecasters)...

and we'll all be subject to lots of LOW PRESSURE at election times.

In the North there'll be lots more...

...ACID RAIN

The End.